DEAR WILLIE..

Your intimate questions answered by an expert

Cartoons and captions by Gray Jolliffe
Text by Peter Mayle

Pan Books
London, Sydney and Auckland

First published in Great Britain in 1989 by
Pan Books Ltd, Cavaye Place, London SW10 9PG
9 8 7 6 5 4 3 2 1
Cartoons and captions © Gray Jolliffe 1989
Text © Peter Mayle 1989
ISBN 0 330 31114 X
Photoset by Parker Typesetting Service, Leicester
Printed and bound in Spain by
Mateu Cromo SA, Madrid

Don't Worry. It's Perfectly Normal

There can be no doubt that the pressures of modern life – career stress, overcrowded cities, high-gravity lager and polyester underwear, to name but a few – have caused an alarming increase in personal problems. Gone are the old uncomplicated days of letting it all hang out, and we now find repressions and complexes wherever we look.

But who can we turn to for sympathy and advice? Psychologists are so expensive that the only people who can afford them are other psychologists. Guidance counsellors are all too busy trying to get on television, while doctors and vicars are desperately trying to keep out of the *News of the World*. And the agony aunts have gone into politics.

It is hardly surprising, therefore, that a vacuum has developed in contemporary society. Fortunately, since nature demands that all vacuums are eventually filled, an unlikely figure has recently emerged as guardian of the nation's intimate secrets. Unfortunately, he is incapable of keeping anything to himself, as this catalogue of deeply confidential aberrations reveals.

YOUR CONSULTANT: SOME PERSONAL NOTES

It is important, when discussing such delicate matters as the relationship between the sexes, to establish the credentials of the guidance counsellor. In this particular case, we can find no evidence of medical or psychological qualifications apart from a fondness for nurses and nude encounter groups. There are, however, certain natural attributes that compensate for any lack of formal training, and they can best be described in the form of a curriculum vitae.

AGE: Permanently 19.

SEX: Whenever possible.

STATUS: Single (even when technically married).

PREVIOUS EXPERIENCE: Garden of Eden, Roman orgies (with distinctions), Harems of all sizes, Charter Membership of several thousand massage parlours, first-class honours in office parties.

HOBBIES: One, and it's not snooker.

OTHER INTERESTS: None.

PERSONALITY PROFILE: Optimistic, single-minded, willing to experiment and to conduct research at any time of day or night, prepared to travel (short distances), outstanding bedside manner.

STATE OF HEALTH: Rude.

AMBITION (*Where would you like to be in five years' time?*): "Same place that I was last night."

From these brief details, it can be seen that we have here a very focussed personality, free from the distractions that have interfered with the work of other eminent sociologists, tireless, dedicated and always on the job. Who could be better qualified to provide advice and comfort to all those who need a shoulder, or something smaller, to cry on?

No wonder I can't get a credit card...

For ease of reference, the material has been arranged in four sections:

○ Fetishes
○ Breakdowns in compatibility
○ Work-related problems
○ Physical difficulties

All names have been withheld for obvious reasons, and we are also holding on to a large bundle of Polaroid photographs sent in by a gentleman from Basingstoke.

FETISHES

Strictly speaking, a fetish is an inanimate object worshipped by savages, such as a totem pole or Ex-President Reagan. Since the publication of the works of Freud, however, it has come to mean something very different. No longer a simple object that you rub to bring you good luck, the fetish now takes many varied and unusual forms, and for some people, such as shoe salesmen, it can even provide a career.

The letters that follow indicate the scope, and in some instances the length, of the fetish in our lives today.

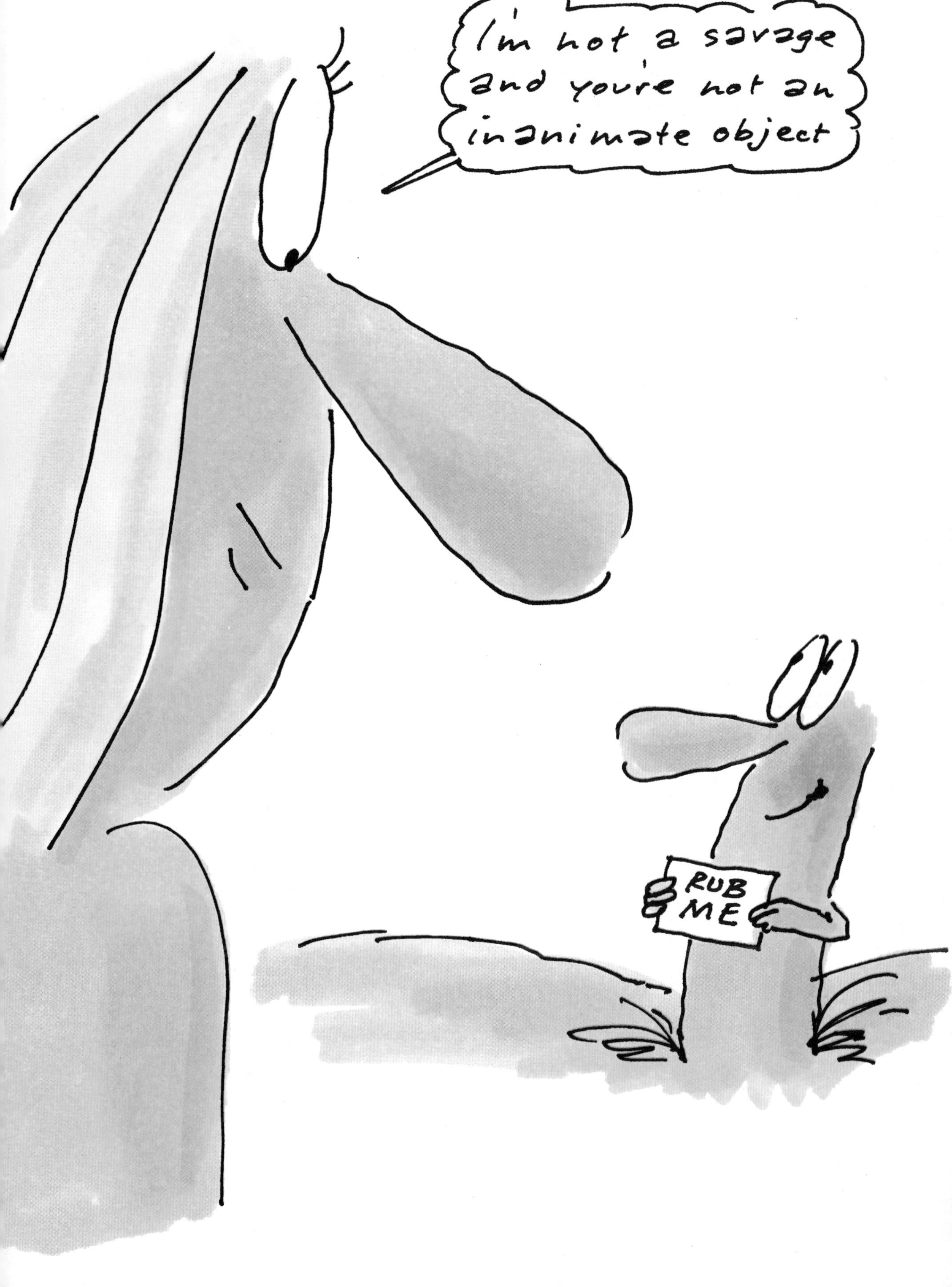
I'm not a savage and you're not an inanimate object
RUB ME

My wife has recently resigned from the Young Conservatives following a disagreement with their policies on law and order. She subsequently gave me for my birthday a burglar's outfit and a policeman's uniform, and every night now it's the same.

With a pair of tights over my head, I have to climb up the drainpipe and through the bedroom window. Then she screams, and while she's dialling 999 I have to change into the policeman's uniform – well, not all of it, actually. Just the boots and helmet. Then she invites me into bed to look for clues.

The problem is that the local constabulary has become involved as a result of her nightly calls, and last week I climbed through the window to find that three of them were already there looking for clues. I coughed to attract my wife's attention, but it was no good, so I changed into the helmet and boots and was arrested for impersonating an officer on duty. To add insult to injury, I noticed that they had taken down my wife's particulars.

I am a reasonable man, fond of animals and ballroom dancing, but I think she has gone too far. What would you do in my position?

"A simple notice would solve your problem:

TRESPASSERS WILL BE CLAMPED AND
TOWED AWAY"

For years, my girl-friend and I have enjoyed many happy and mutually satisfying hours playing doctors and nurses. I have given her everything she could wish for – crepe-soled shoes, surgical stockings, a personalised thermometer and even her own operating table – but now she is making demands that threaten our whole relationship. It's no good. I can't give her an index-linked rise every time she feels like it, and it's ruining my health. Have any other readers experienced similar problems?

"This is not at all uncommon, and can usually be
relieved by a period of rest. If this is not
possible, have you considered using a splint?
The NHS model is virtually undetectable in use,
and comes in a range of pastel colours as well as
the exciting new matt black finish."

I have tried all kinds of things to bring back the sparkle in our sex life, but my husband never responded until I came home with a schoolgirl's gym-slip. The trouble is he refuses to take it off, and I am worried what the people at work will say. Also, the neighbours are starting to talk. What can I tell them?

"Don't let mischievous gossip stand between you and personal fulfilment. Remember that your happiness comes first, no matter what the neighbours may say. The only thing to watch out for is if the blonde next door starts offering your husband sweets while he's waiting at the bus stop."

I have always admired artistic people, and so I was very pleased when my boy-friend took up photography. How was I to know it would affect him like this? He's thrown away the nice pyjamas I gave him last Christmas and now comes to bed with a black cloth over his head and keeps shouting 'watch the birdie!'
Yesterday he bought an adjustable tripod. What can he be planning to do?

"That's no tripod. You should be so lucky."

My husband was educated at a well-known public school, and therefore has great difficulty in certain aspects of our personal life unless I give him a cold bath and a good spanking first. Now he has started bringing several old school friends home with him, and I find I just can't cope. Do you think it would upset our relationship if I asked the cleaning lady to give me a hand?

"The need for discipline far outweighs any other considerations. Naughty boys must be punished, and they will appreciate another firm hand. Introduce the cleaning lady as your Head Prefect, and if you should need any more help, call in the local hockey team."

I am writing this with some difficulty as my husband has tied me to the bed, which he does every Friday night. I usually find this quite stimulating – specially the bit where he cuts me free with his Boy Scout knife – but I am beginning to worry that the magic has gone out of our marriage. Last Friday he tied me up and went down to the pub. Now he's gone off to Brighton for the weekend. He says it is extended foreplay, but I'm not so sure.

"It sounds as though he is taking advantage of your good nature and your inability to untie knots, but you can never tell. Today it's a weekend in Brighton; tomorrow it might be two weeks in Torremolinos, or a round-the-world cruise, and then where will you be? It's time to put your foot down if he hasn't tied it up. Why don't you suggest changing places?"

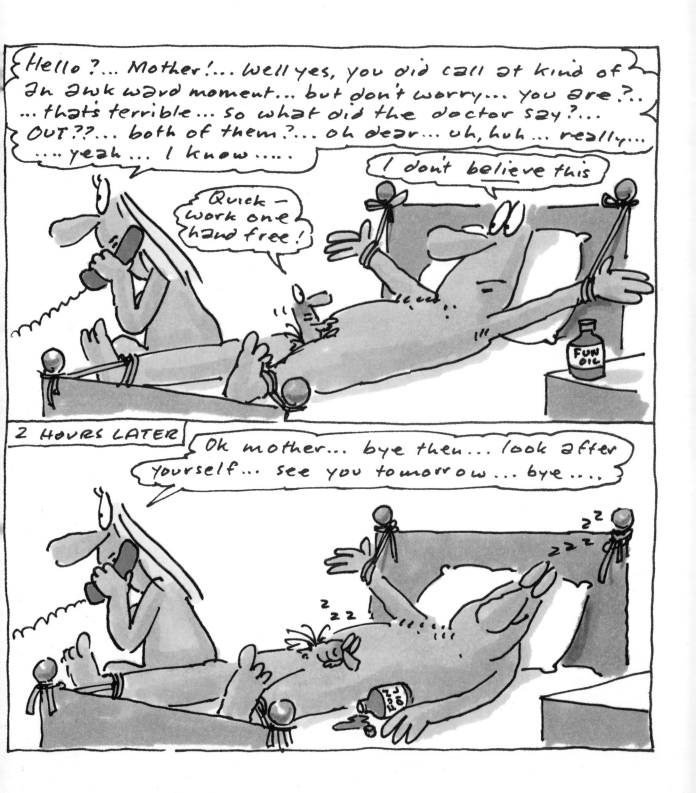

BREAKDOWNS IN COMPATIBILITY

As a result of the shorter working week and a corresponding increase in leisure time, we can now devote much more attention to our loved ones and the pursuit of meaningful relationships. This, of course, brings problems of its own. It is no coincidence that America, the home of the meaningful relationship, has a higher divorce rate and more complexes per square couple than anywhere else in the world.

But we are catching up. . . .

What would you like as an anniversary present?
A divorce
I dont think he had anything that expensive in mind

On the whole, my boy-friend is sensitive and
caring, but he doesn't seem to realise that there
are times when he has to put my feelings and
needs before his own. I don't expect it every
night, but it would make such a difference to
our relationship if sometimes he would let me
have my headache before he has his. It's all
over so quickly, and he's in the bathroom
looking for the aspirin while I'm left high and
dry. I've tried talking to him, but he says it's
something wrong with me. The girls at work all
have headaches two or three times a week, and
hearing them talk about it makes me even more
depressed and irritable. They have suggested
medical advice, but I'd rather not go under the
doctor, who is a friend of the family.

"Premature migraine, as it is known in medical circles, is usually caused by nervous anxiety, and the difficulties you are experiencing have arisen for one simple reason: you just aren't anxious enough. Try to worry about something before going to bed – the ozone layer, those stubborn washday stains, even your ability to achieve a satisfactory headache – and you will soon find yourself sufficiently tense to respond to your boy-friend. From there, it is only a short step to achieving your headaches together – the mutual migraine. To prolong the experience, hide the aspirin."

My wife and I have always been fond of a little musical accompaniment during our moments of passion, and I still get the old tingle whenever I hear the first few bars of Ravel's Bolero. But she is now saying that we should be more imaginative, and insists on playing the Dance of the Sugar Plum Fairy which I find puts me right off my stroke. We have tried separate headphones, but my *andante* never quite fits in with her *fortissimo*, and we are finding it increasingly difficult to arrive at the finale at the same time. Would a conductor help?

"Conductors have a nasty habit of bringing in
the wind section and wanting to sign
autographs afterwards. You would be far better
off if you made more imaginative use of your
very own conductor's baton."

All our friends said it was a perfect match when we got married, as I was a voyeur and he was an exhibitionist. I suppose I should never have sent his raincoat to the cleaners, because ever since then he has been a changed man. Now he's become a voyeur too, and all we do is sit and look at each other. I got quite tearful when I found his raincoat and those special trousers bundled up in the corner of the wardrobe. We went out to the park together the other night and I made him hide in the bushes, but even that didn't work. We are both in our early twenties and hope one day to have a family. But how?

"This is a temporary condition most often found during the cold months of winter, when exposure to the elements can be uncomfortable and sometimes very serious (as in the famous case of the Blue Man of Wimbledon Common). Five minutes with a well-aimed blow heater will work wonders."

It all started harmlessly enough when my wife began reading the Sunday papers out loud while we were having early morning tea. At first we used to laugh at the stories, but then she began to drop hints about other couples having more exciting sex lives and now I keep finding naked men under the bed. My wife says it's nothing serious, and I hope it's just a phase she's going through. Do you think I should change to the *Sunday Telegraph*?

"Even the *Telegraph* won't help these days,
unless you cut out the more racy passages in the
Court Circular. Try shock tactics! Fight fire with
fire! Put a naked woman under your side of the
bed and see what happens."

My husband always rolls over and goes to sleep afterwards, which makes me feel like a discarded sex object, only good for one thing. His excuse is that he's had a hard day at the office, but what about me? Don't I deserve some consideration? I've mentioned this to my neighbour, but she says I'm lucky; her husband is asleep before she's even finished putting her curlers in. Is romance dead?

"Many husbands are known to suffer from this complaint, which is usually accompanied by loud snoring. So far, therapists have been unable to suggest anything other than narrower beds (which make rolling over physically dangerous), or hitting the brute over the head with a pillow to wake him up. In extreme cases, try a bedside lamp."

WORK RELATED PROBLEMS

It has often been said that ambitious men and women never really leave the office. Consciously or subconsciously, they bring their work home with them, and it has been known for them to bring their secretaries back as well to attend to some unfinished dictation.

Fortunately, such cases are rare, but it is all too common for the cares of office to affect every aspect of a couple's personal life. From the taxi driver to the captain of industry, we all suffer from what psychologists describe as vocational pressures, which often manifest themselves at bedtime in the most unexpected ways. Who will ever forget the extraordinary case of the belly dancer and the gynaecologist, for instance? And who can read the uncensored letters that follow without recognising someone they know? Or worse still, someone they live with?

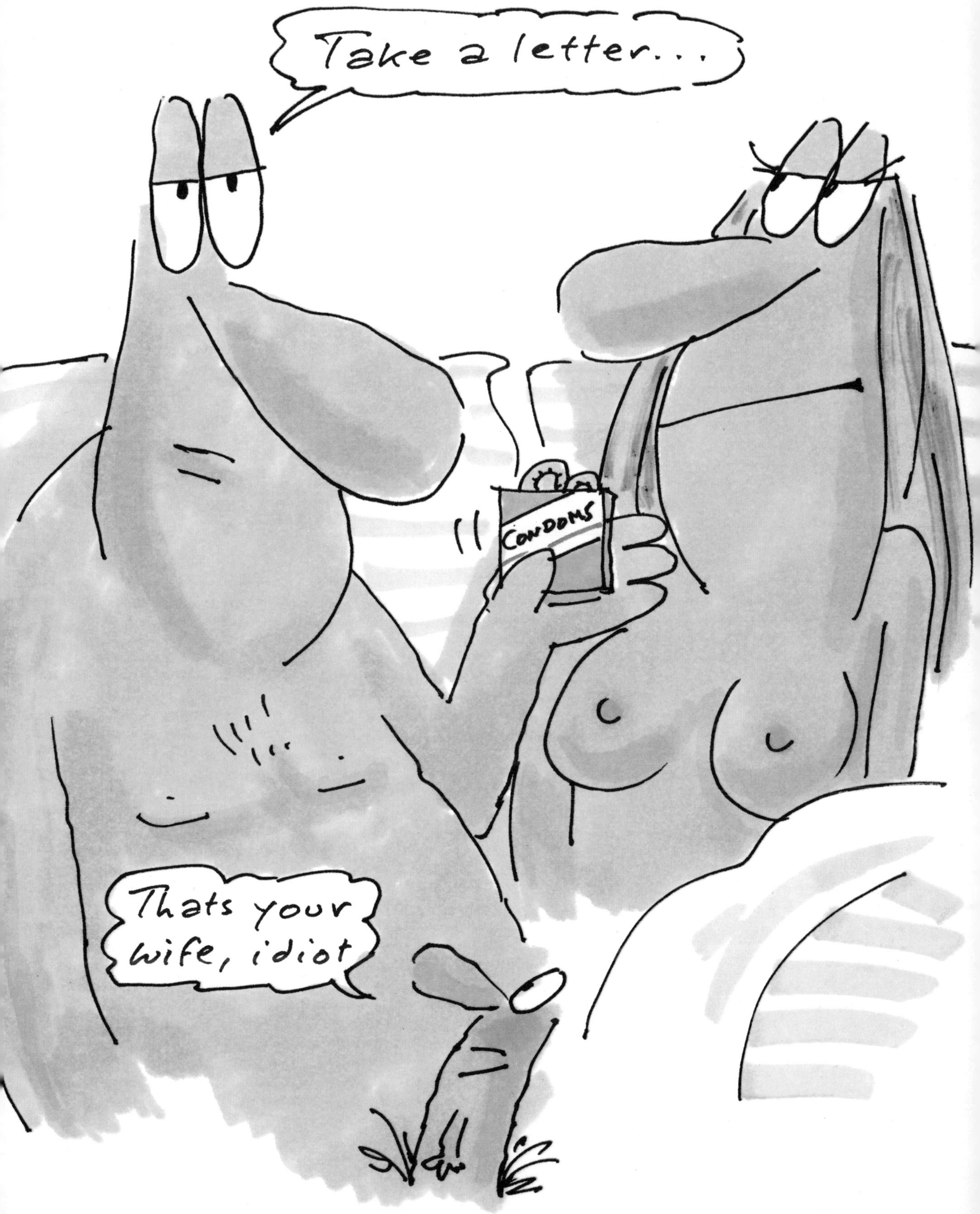
Take a letter...
CONDOMS
Thats your wife, idiot

My boy-friend's old job as a window dresser in Oxford Street made us break up because he could not stop adjusting me, and I used to get terrible pins and needles from standing still so long. When he changed jobs we got back together again, and for a few weeks he was a different person. Now he is back to his old tricks, and cannot seem to forget that he is a figure-skating judge. He grades me on interpretation, freestyle and balance, and keeps jumping out of bed to hold his score cards up at the window. The people in the house opposite say it's better than the television and have started to invite their friends around to watch. Every time I suggest that my boy-friend finds another job he gives me nought out of ten. I used to be a happy, fun-loving girl, but now I dread putting on my skates every night. Can you introduce me to a nice accountant?

"How about a nice guidance counsellor instead?
Send in your telephone number and a recent
photograph, which will be treated in the strictest
confidence. Who knows? We could end up as
Torville and Willie."

You see all kinds of things in my line of work, driving a cab. Passengers don't realise I know what they are getting up to. Downright disgusting it is sometimes. Talk about acrobatics. Anyway, I think it's beginning to get to me, because the only way I can get frisky nowadays is to sit on the end of the bed and watch my old lady through a rear view mirror until my meter starts running. What I'd really like to do is to get her in the back of the cab, but she isn't having any. Nothing wrong with that, is there? All good clean fun. Thank you for not smoking.

"Any dramatic change in your sexual habits, such as the one you describe, should be approached gradually. Your wife is probably worried about getting a parking ticket. Promise her you won't try anything in crowded thoroughfares such as Leicester Square on Saturday night. Pick a deserted spot, turn off your meter and don't ask for a tip afterwards."

I had only been out twice with this film director when he asked me back to his flat to watch an erotic video. I was nervous at first, but when he said he could find me a part in his next production, I decided to treat the experience as a career move. As a matter of fact, I was quite looking forward to it. What a let-down! Every time we got to one of those artistic bits where the heroine is about to give her all, he pushed a freeze-frame button and starting talking about the lighting and the camera angles. Next thing I know, he is telling me about someone called a focus-puller. Well, I'm not a prude, but I draw the line at that sort of language. All the same, I really like him, and there's always the chance of a big part. Now he's asked me if I want to see his retrospective. What should I do?

"There is nothing unnatural or harmful about retrospectives providing they don't become a habit. Your boy-friend is obviously shy and finds it difficult to express his true feelings outside the context of his film work. Be patient with him, and keep a clapper-board in your handbag in case things get out of hand."

Ever since she started working in the gift-wrapping department at Selfridges my wife has been behaving very strangely. She says she needs practice at wrapping unusually-shaped objects. I won't go into details, but it is embarrassing and often rather painful when she gets carried away with the aerosol of spray-on glitter. I would like to encourage her in her career, but I am developing a nasty rash and a horror of crinkly ribbons. Christmas is coming and my wife is talking about tinsel and holly leaves. How can I stop her? I don't want to hurt her feelings, but mine are very sore.

"A Santa Claus outfit is warm, comfortable and provides excellent protection. If threatened with silver and red balls, run for the chimney."

I am a very busy and important man, and it is
essential that I have my personal secretary with
me at all times. After all, who knows when I
might have a flash of inspiration, and someone
must be on hand to take it down. My wife, very
unreasonably I think, has just sent me a memo
objecting to my secretary's presence in the
bedroom, even though she sits quietly in the
corner. What's the matter with the silly woman?
She won't come to my office to discuss it, and is
refusing to merge with me. Should I withdraw
my majority holding?

"Show her your voting shares, and try a
takeover. If that fails, maybe she would accept a
golden handshake."

PHYSICAL DIFFICULTIES

A well-known film actress once complained as follows: 'The conventional position makes me claustrophobic. And the others either give me a stiff neck or lockjaw.'

Many eminent figures, from sex therapists to physical training instructors, have tried to work out exactly what she was talking about, since anything that men and women do so frequently should in theory be fairly straightforward. Fresh evidence, however, indicates that this is not the case. Far from the joyous, carefree rapture that we read about in romantic novels and the memoirs of cabinet ministers, it appears that most people have to overcome serious obstacles in their pursuit of perfect bliss.

Television-related problems come high on the list, followed closely by withdrawal symptoms induced by lager and the after-effects of curry dinners. But it doesn't stop there. Even the choice of bedroom furniture can interfere with the course of true love, as these revealing communications show.

My wife and I are keen viewers of a programme
called Come Dancing, but try as we might we
have never been able to do it. What's the secret?

"Rumba lessons."

Rambo, our pedigree Alsatian, has suddenly
turned very jealous, and growls whenever my
husband tries to get into bed. We hoped he was
just being playful, but last week he bit what he
thought was a bone, and my husband had to
have several stitches and is still being treated
for shock. He seems quite comfortable tucked
up in Rambo's basket, but we can't go on like
this. The vet has suggested that we buy Rambo
a squeaky toy, but I think he prefers the real
thing.

"If you can manage to find a postman's leg in good condition, that might provide a tasty alternative. Otherwise, call in your local taxidermist, but make sure he only stuffs the dog."

After watching one of those cookery programmes on TV, my wife has started to experiment with what she calls warming up her little leftover. I like toad-in-the-hole as much as the next man, but I object to being treated like a rissole. When I made my feelings clear to my wife, she just sprinkled me with cayenne pepper and told me I was lucky she wasn't a vegetarian. Now she's talking about kebabs, and I have nightmares about being rolled up in strips of bacon. For all I know, she might be considering sausage rolls. I'm desperate.

"This condition was first diagnosed many years ago as night starvation, and eventually cured by massive doses of curry powder, administered locally. Don't worry. The inflammation is only temporary."

I have often read about people smoking after sex, but all we ever seem to manage is slight perspiration. Are we doing something wrong?

"This is a bit of artistic licence, and you shouldn't take it literally. The best that most of us can manage is a certain amount of steam. Keep trying."

We tried a water bed, but my girl-friend said it made her seasick. Then we tried satin sheets, but she kept slipping off the bed. Now at great expense I have turned the ceiling into a giant mirror, but she says it's too far away to do her makeup. I'm beginning to think that she doesn't find me physically attractive. Is there any way I can find out for sure before I invest in a pair of leather pyjamas?

"Your girl-friend is obviously trying to tell you something, but doesn't want to upset you. Ask her if there's something she wants to get off her chest, and don't be too disappointed if she says it's you."

I am married to someone who thinks that foreplay is 18 pints of Stella Artois and a quick tandoori before coming home to throw me on the bed. In every other respect, she is a lovely girl, and I would like to save our marriage, but the last time I tried to get her to change her ways she gave me a black eye with her crash helmet. How can I appeal to her better nature, which I know is hidden somewhere beneath her motor bike outfit?

"Karate lessons."

CLASSIFIED SECTION: LONELY HEARTS AND OTHER PARTS

Sado-masochist, own chains and equipment, seeks female winch operator with similar interests.

Large selection of married men always available for extra-marital affairs. Contact the social secretary, House of Commons, Westminster.

Organ lessons. Professor Rita, Soho Academy of Music.

Must sell thigh boots and whip due to change in personal circumstances. Would consider exchanging for nurse's uniform in mint condition.

Kama Sutra enthusiast with bad back seeks bright, attractive physiotherapist with impressive qualifications (minimum 38 inches).

Fun-loving chiropodist will make house calls on gentlemen in distress. Who said high heels have to hurt? Deportment lessons for a small extra charge.

Fed up with waiting for the phone to ring? Mature, experienced heavy breather offers round-the-clock service.

Say it with condoms! Wide range of colours and patterns, including luminous. Give him one and watch him light up.

The publishers cannot accept any responsibility for the goods and services offered, and readers are advised to check with their doctor (early forties, distinguished appearance, fond of dressing up) before undergoing any extended treatment.

DO-IT-YOURSELF THERAPY

Here is a chance to assess your abilities as a guidance counsellor. Beneath each of the carefully selected questions which follow, you will find multiple-choice answers. Tick those that you feel most helpful and appropriate, and send them in to Wicked Willie, Pan Books, Cavaye Place, London. Results will be judged by a panel of eminent bodily functions specialists, and the winner will be eligible for a) a weekend in Basingstoke with Miss Fanshawe from stock control, or b) the cash equivalent.

'I have met this boy at work, and would really like to get to know him, but he only seems to be interested in football. How can I make him notice me?'

A Show him your referee's whistle.
B Ask him to show you *his* referee's whistle.
C Go in for a low tackle.

'Although I have a BSc. in Hairdressing and have read several of Jeffrey Archer's books, men never take me seriously. How can I show them that I have a brain as well as a body?'

A Try wearing bigger sweaters.
B Never bend over in mixed company.
C Let's have dinner at my place and talk about it.

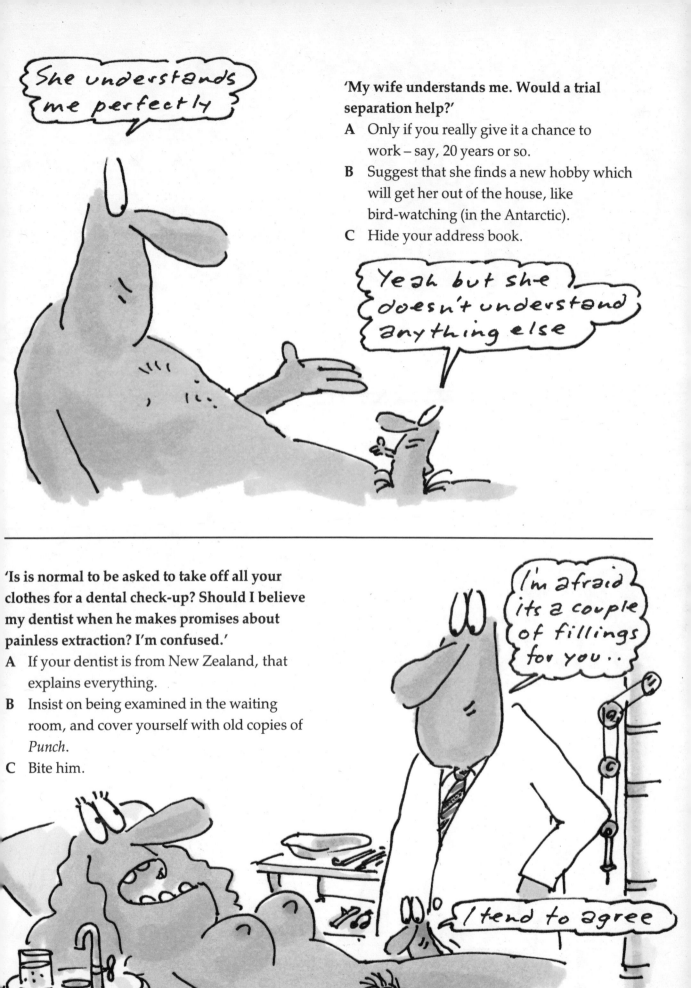

'My wife understands me. Would a trial separation help?'

A   Only if you really give it a chance to work – say, 20 years or so.

B   Suggest that she finds a new hobby which will get her out of the house, like bird-watching (in the Antarctic).

C   Hide your address book.

'Is is normal to be asked to take off all your clothes for a dental check-up? Should I believe my dentist when he makes promises about painless extraction? I'm confused.'

A   If your dentist is from New Zealand, that explains everything.

B   Insist on being examined in the waiting room, and cover yourself with old copies of *Punch*.

C   Bite him.

'Is it possible to love two women at the same time?'

A Yes.
B No.
C Only if you're very fit.

'I have started going out with an older man. I had hoped it was going to be a purely physical relationship, but recently he's been making suggestive remarks about a platonic friendship. How can I put a stop to this before it goes too far?'

A Tell him tactfully not to rush things.
B Don't let yourself be put in platonic situations – i.e. visits to the Public Library, tea with his auntie.
C Try wearing tighter sweaters.

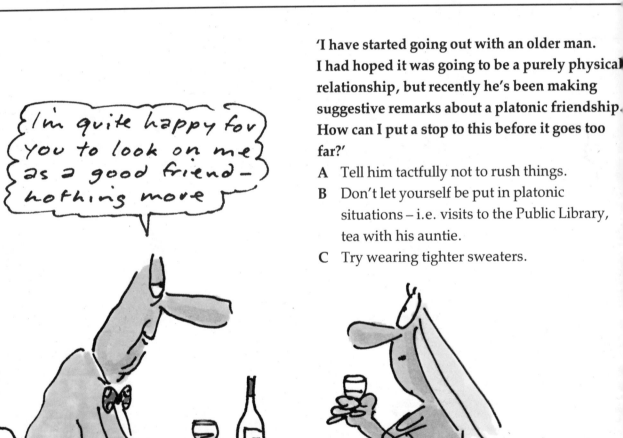

'My wife and I have been invited to go on holiday with another couple. We thought we were going pony-trekking, but now they say they've booked us all in to a nudist colony outside Skegness. We're embarrassed, because we don't really know them that well.'

A You will.
B Pack some warm socks.
C Tell them you can't go because you're vegetarians.

'There's a man at my health club who keeps talking about mixed doubles. I've told him I don't play tennis, but he says that doesn't matter. What do you think he means?'

A Something they don't do on the Centre Court.
B If you decide to try it, bring your own umpire.
C Stay out of the sauna.

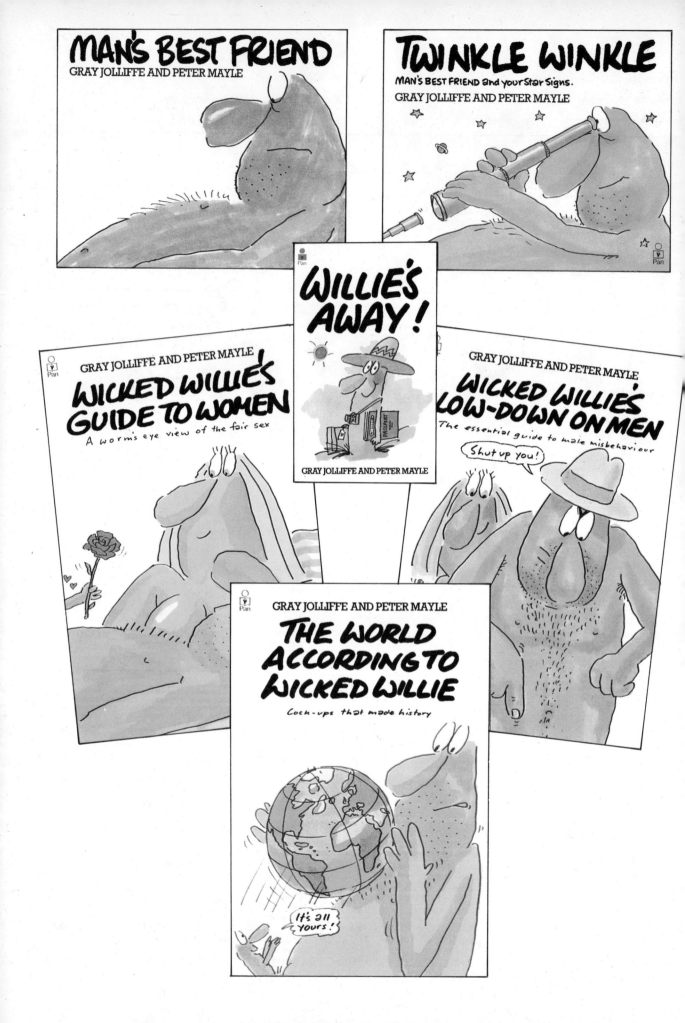

ALSO AVAILABLE IN PAN